The Far Side

Millennium

Desk Calendar 2000

Gary Larson

Andrews McMeel
Publishing

an Andrews McMeel Universal company
Kansas City

www.andrewsmcmeel.com

ISBN: 0-8362-9907-8

Few periods in history have been spared humiliation at the hands of The Far Side®. Inspired by the approach of a new millennium, we have seized this opportunity to use Gary Larson's ageless wit to impart a little historical knowledge. We gathered fifty-three Far Side cartoons and matched them with facts about often overlooked historical events from the last millennium. The watercolored cartoons and the quirky trivia are arranged chronologically to present an entertaining, if not complete, history of the last thousand years. So laugh, learn, and lay out your days, all with *The Far Side® Millennium Desk Calendar 2000.*

January

Sunday	Monday	Tuesday	Wednesday	Thursday	Friday	Saturday
26	27	28	29	30	31	1 New Year's Day Kwanzaa ends
2	3	4	5	6	7	8
9	10	11	12	13	14	15
16	17 Martin Luther King Jr.'s Birthday (observed)	18	19	20	21	22
23	24	25	26	27	28	29
30	31					

December 1999

S	M	T	W	T	F	S
28	29	30	1	2	3	4
5	6	7	8	9	10	11
12	13	14	15	16	17	18
19	20	21	22	23	24	25
26	27	28	29	30	31	1

February

S	M	T	W	T	F	S
30	31	1	2	3	4	5
6	7	8	9	10	11	12
13	14	15	16	17	18	19
20	21	22	23	24	25	26
27	28	29	1	2	3	4

Important Dates/Notes

"Everyone can just put down their loot and plunder, and Sven here—yes, old Sven, who was in charge of reading the tide chart—has something to say to us all."

December 1999-January 2000

1003

Vikings begin a three-year visit to the northern continent in the Western Hemisphere. (Indigenous people thought it was going to be only for a couple of weeks.)

Notes

| Monday | 27 |

| Tuesday | 28 |

| Wednesday | 29 |

| Thursday | 30 |

| Friday | 31 |

| Saturday | 1 |

New Year's Day
Kwanzaa ends

| Sunday | 2 |

January

S	M	T	W	T	F	S
26	27	28	29	30	31	1
2	3	4	5	6	7	8
9	10	11	12	13	14	15
16	17	18	19	20	21	22
23 30	24 31	25	26	27	28	29

"You're kidding! ... I was struck twice by lightning too!"

January

Notes

Monday	3

Tuesday	4

Wednesday	5

Thursday	6

Friday	7

Saturday	8

Sunday	9

January

S	M	T	W	T	F	S
26	27	28	29	30	31	1
2	3	4	5	6	7	8
9	10	11	12	13	14	15
16	17	18	19	20	21	22
23 30	24 31	25	26	27	28	29

Suddenly, a heated exchange took place between the king and the moat contractor.

January

1078
Construction of the Tower of London begins. In its lifetime it will house a zoo, observatory, mint, prison, royal palace, and is now home of the crown jewels. (It's rumored that both The Gap and Starbucks are currently vying for the space.)

SPACE FOR LEASE
CONTACT THE QUEEN

Notes

_____

_____

_____

_____

_____

_____

_____

_____

_____

January

S	M	T	W	T	F	S
26	27	28	29	30	31	1
2	3	4	5	6	7	8
9	10	11	12	13	14	15
16	17	18	19	20	21	22
23 / 30	24 / 31	25	26	27	28	29

Monday 10

Tuesday 11

Wednesday 12

Thursday 13

Friday 14

Saturday 15

Sunday 16

"This ain't gonna look good on our report, Leroy."

January

1176
Rabbits are introduced into England as domestic livestock, and they quickly populate the entire British Isles. (Duh.)

Notes

_____

_____

_____

_____

_____

_____

_____

_____

January

S	M	T	W	T	F	S
26	27	28	29	30	31	1
2	3	4	5	6	7	8
9	10	11	12	13	14	15
16	17	18	19	20	21	22
23 30	24 31	25	26	27	28	29

Monday   17

Martin Luther King Jr.'s Birthday (observed)
Tuesday   18

Wednesday   19

Thursday   20

Friday   21

Saturday   22

Sunday   23

"Of course, living in an all-glass house has its disadvantages ...
but you should see the birds smack it."

January

1180

Glass windows appear in private English houses. (Shortly after, the first housekeeper is chronicled as saying, "I don't do windows.")

Notes

_____

_____

_____

_____

_____

_____

_____

_____

_____

January

S	M	T	W	T	F	S
26	27	28	29	30	31	1
2	3	4	5	6	7	8
9	10	11	12	13	14	15
16	17	18	19	20	21	22
23 30	24 31	25	26	27	28	29

Monday   24

Tuesday   25

Wednesday   26

Thursday   27

Friday   28

Saturday   29

Sunday   30

February

Sunday	Monday	Tuesday	Wednesday	Thursday	Friday	Saturday
30	31	1	2	3	4	5
			Groundhog Day			
6	7	8	9	10	11	12
13	14	15	16	17	18	19
	Valentine's Day					
20	21	22	23	24	25	26
	Presidents' Day					
27	28	29	1	2	3	4

January

S	M	T	W	T	F	S
26	27	28	29	30	31	1
2	3	4	5	6	7	8
9	10	11	12	13	14	15
16	17	18	19	20	21	22
23	24	25	26	27	28	29
30	31					

March

S	M	T	W	T	F	S
27	28	29	1	2	3	4
5	6	7	8	9	10	11
12	13	14	15	16	17	18
19	20	21	22	23	24	25
26	27	28	29	30	31	1

Important Dates/Notes

In what was destined to be a short-lived spectacle, a chicken, suspended
by a balloon, floated through the Samurai bar's doorway.

January-February

1185

Sixty-year-old Samurai Saito Sanemori, a loyal soldier to the emperor, dyes his hair black before battle so as not to feel inferior to the younger warriors (although, as far as we know, no one has ever said, "Hey, old-timer!" to a Samurai).

Notes

_____
_____
_____
_____
_____
_____
_____
_____
_____
_____
_____

February

S	M	T	W	T	F	S
30	31	1	2	3	4	5
6	7	8	9	10	11	12
13	14	15	16	17	18	19
20	21	22	23	24	25	26
27	28	29	1	2	3	4

Monday 31

Tuesday 1

Wednesday 2

Groundhog Day
Thursday 3

Friday 4

Saturday 5

Sunday 6

Rhino recitals

February

1221
The sonnet form develops in Italian poetry. (Allegedly, it all starts with "Roses are red ... ")

Notes

_____

_____

_____

_____

_____

_____

_____

_____

February

S	M	T	W	T	F	S
30	31	1	2	3	4	5
6	7	8	9	10	11	12
13	14	15	16	17	18	19
20	21	22	23	24	25	26
27	28	29	1	2	3	4

Monday 7

Tuesday 8

Wednesday 9

Thursday 10

Friday 11

Saturday 12

Sunday 13

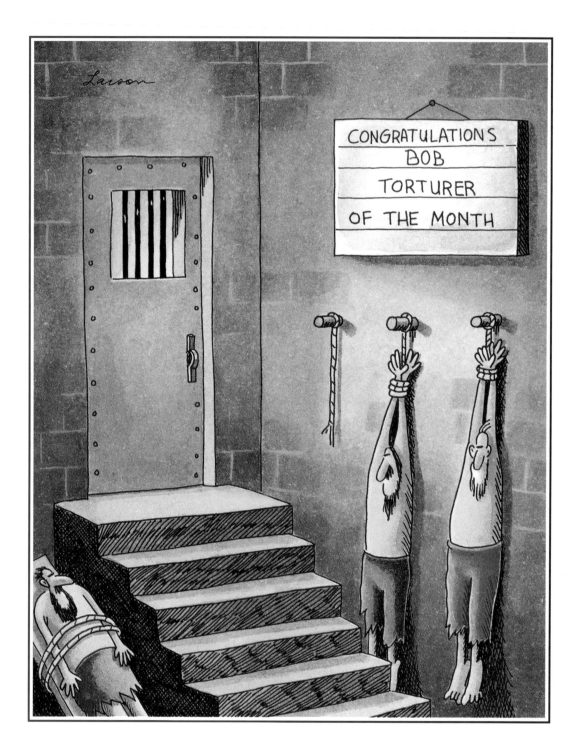

February

Monday   14

Valentine's Day

Tuesday   15

Notes

_____

_____

_____

_____

_____

_____

_____

Wednesday   16

Thursday   17

Friday   18

Saturday   19

Sunday   20

February

S	M	T	W	T	F	S
30	31	1	2	3	4	5
6	7	8	9	10	11	12
13	14	15	16	17	18	19
20	21	22	23	24	25	26
27	28	29	1	2	3	4

"For crying out loud, Doris. ... You gotta drag that thing out every time we all get together?"

February

1267

The principles of a camera that can project pictures are first described by Roger Bacon. (Unfortunately, in 1267, film is hard to come by.)

Notes

_____

_____

_____

_____

_____

_____

_____

_____

_____

February

S	M	T	W	T	F	S
30	31	1	2	3	4	5
6	7	8	9	10	11	12
13	14	15	16	17	18	19
20	21	22	23	24	25	26
27	28	29	1	2	3	4

Monday 21

Presidents' Day
Tuesday 22

Wednesday 23

Thursday 24

Friday 25

Saturday 26

Sunday 27

March

Sunday	Monday	Tuesday	Wednesday	Thursday	Friday	Saturday
27	28	29	1	2	3	4
5	6	7	8 Ash Wednesday	9	10	11
12	13	14	15	16	17 St. Patrick's Day	18
19	20	21 Purim	22	23	24	25
26	27	28	29	30	31	1

February

S	M	T	W	T	F	S
30	31	1	2	3	4	5
6	7	8	9	10	11	12
13	14	15	16	17	18	19
20	21	22	23	24	25	26
27	28	29	1	2	3	4

April

S	M	T	W	T	F	S
26	27	28	29	30	31	1
2	3	4	5	6	7	8
9	10	11	12	13	14	15
16	17	18	19	20	21	22
23 / 30	24	25	26	27	28	29

Important Dates/Notes

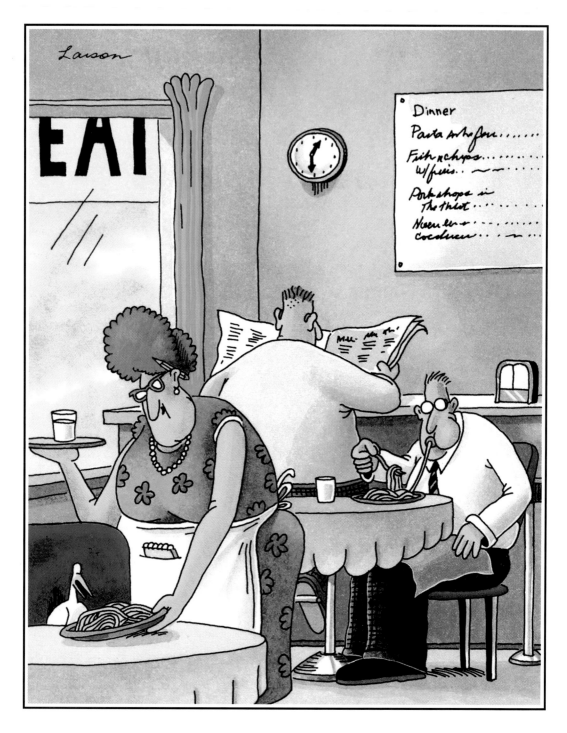

"Whoa! This just looks like regular spaghetti! ...
Where's my Earthworms Alfredo?"

February-March

1284

avioli is first introduced to Romans, who previously enjoyed mostly fettucini as their primary pasta. (Both, however, come with a side of vegetables.)

Notes

Monday	28

Tuesday	29

Wednesday	1

Thursday	2

Friday	3

Saturday	4

Sunday	5

March

S	M	T	W	T	F	S
27	28	29	1	2	3	4
5	6	7	8	9	10	11
12	13	14	15	16	17	18
19	20	21	22	23	24	25
26	27	28	29	30	31	1

"Hey! *You* don't tell *me* what makes 'er tick!
I know what makes 'er tick, sonny boy!"

March

Notes

Monday	6

Tuesday	7

Wednesday	8

Ash Wednesday

Thursday	9

Friday	10

Saturday	11

Sunday	12

March

S	M	T	W	T	F	S
27	28	29	1	2	3	4
5	6	7	8	9	10	11
12	13	14	15	16	17	18
19	20	21	22	23	24	25
26	27	28	29	30	31	1

"Wait a minute here, Mr. Crumbley. ... Maybe it isn't kidney stones after all."

March

1300

Urine examination as a means of diagnosis is first used in medicine. (Skeptics pooh-pooh the practice.)

Notes

March

S	M	T	W	T	F	S
27	28	29	1	2	3	4
5	6	7	8	9	10	11
12	13	14	15	16	17	18
19	20	21	22	23	24	25
26	27	28	29	30	31	1

Monday 13

Tuesday 14

Wednesday 15

Thursday 16

Friday 17

St. Patrick's Day
Saturday 18

Sunday 19

Unknown to most historians, William Tell had an older
and less fortunate son named Warren.

March

Notes

Monday	20

Tuesday	21

Perim

Wednesday	22

Thursday	23

Friday	24

Saturday	25

Sunday	26

March

S	M	T	W	T	F	S
27	28	29	1	2	3	4
5	6	7	8	9	10	11
12	13	14	15	16	17	18
19	20	21	22	23	24	25
26	27	28	29	30	31	1

April

Sunday	Monday	Tuesday	Wednesday	Thursday	Friday	Saturday
26	27	28	29	30	31	1
2	3	4	5	6	7	8
9	10	11	12	13	14	15
16 Palm Sunday	17	18	19	20 Passover	21 Good Friday	22
23 Easter	24 Easter Monday (Canada)	25	26	27	28	29
30						

March

S	M	T	W	T	F	S
27	28	29	1	2	3	4
5	6	7	8	9	10	11
12	13	14	15	16	17	18
19	20	21	22	23	24	25
26	27	28	29	30	31	1

May

S	M	T	W	T	F	S
30	1	2	3	4	5	6
7	8	9	10	11	12	13
14	15	16	17	18	19	20
21	22	23	24	25	26	27
28	29	30	31	1	2	3

Important Dates/Notes

Quasimodo ends his day.

March-April

1345

After 182 years of construction, the Gothic-style cathedral of Notre Dame in Paris is completed. (Hipster critics complain, "Goth is so twelve-hundreds!")

Notes

April

S	M	T	W	T	F	S
26	27	28	29	30	31	1
2	3	4	5	6	7	8
9	10	11	12	13	14	15
16	17	18	19	20	21	22
23 30	24	25	26	27	28	29

Monday 27

Tuesday 28

Wednesday 29

Thursday 30

Friday 31

Saturday 1

Sunday 2

"Uh-oh."

April

According to doctors at the University of Paris, the plague is caused by "a triple conjunction of Saturn, Jupiter, and Mars in the 40th degree of Aquarius." (Such medical hypotheses give rise to the advice, "Get a second opinion.")

Notes

April

S	M	T	W	T	F	S
26	27	28	29	30	31	1
2	3	4	5	6	7	8
9	10	11	12	13	14	15
16	17	18	19	20	21	22
23 / 30	24	25	26	27	28	29

Monday   3

Tuesday   4

Wednesday   5

Thursday   6

Friday   7

Saturday   8

Sunday   9

Vern waited, hoping to God for one moment—one precious moment—
when the herd would cluster together.

April

Notes

April						
S	M	T	W	T	F	S
26	27	28	29	30	31	1
2	3	4	5	6	7	8
9	10	11	12	13	14	15
16	17	18	19	20	21	22
23 / 30	24	25	26	27	28	29

Monday 10

Tuesday 11

Wednesday 12

Thursday 13

Friday 14

Saturday 15

Sunday 16

Palm Sunday

"Those, sire, are the uncommon folk."

April

1381

The Peasants Revolt finally begins in England 30 years after Parliament passes the Statute of Labourers, holding down wages and arousing resentment among the slow-to-anger peasants.

REVOLUTION!

Notes

April

S	M	T	W	T	F	S
26	27	28	29	30	31	1
2	3	4	5	6	7	8
9	10	11	12	13	14	15
16	17	18	19	20	21	22
23/30	24	25	26	27	28	29

Monday 17

Tuesday 18

Wednesday 19

Thursday 20

Passover
Friday 21

Good Friday
Saturday 22

Sunday 23

Easter

Carmen Miranda's family reunion

April

Notes

April

S	M	T	W	T	F	S
26	27	28	29	30	31	1
2	3	4	5	6	7	8
9	10	11	12	13	14	15
16	17	18	19	20	21	22
23 30	24	25	26	27	28	29

Monday 24

Easter Monday (Canada)
Tuesday 25

Wednesday 26

Thursday 27

Friday 28

Saturday 29

Sunday 30

May

Sunday	Monday	Tuesday	Wednesday	Thursday	Friday	Saturday
30	1	2	3	4	5	6
7	8	9	10	11	12	13
14 Mother's Day	15	16	17	18	19	20 Armed Forces Day
21	22 Victoria Day (Canada)	23	24	25	26	27
28	29 Memorial Day	30	31	1	2	3

April

S	M	T	W	T	F	S
26	27	28	29	30	31	1
2	3	4	5	6	7	8
9	10	11	12	13	14	15
16	17	18	19	20	21	22
23 30	24	25	26	27	28	29

June

S	M	T	W	T	F	S
28	29	30	31	1	2	3
4	5	6	7	8	9	10
11	12	13	14	15	16	17
18	19	20	21	22	23	24
25	26	27	28	29	30	1

Important Dates/Notes

May

1420

A pack of wolves roams the streets of Paris, entering the city from the nearby forest. (It was the last time such a thing ever happened and was probably just some kind of animal dare.)

PARIS

Notes

| Monday | 1 |

| Tuesday | 2 |

| Wednesday | 3 |

| Thursday | 4 |

| Friday | 5 |

| Saturday | 6 |

| Sunday | 7 |

May

S	M	T	W	T	F	S
30	1	2	3	4	5	6
7	8	9	10	11	12	13
14	15	16	17	18	19	20
21	22	23	24	25	26	27
28	29	30	31	1	2	3

"Oh, wait! Wait, Cory! ... Add the cereal *first* and *then* the milk!"

May

1472

Vatican librarian Platina's *De Honesta Voluptate* (*Concerning Honest Pleasure and Well-Being*), the first printed cookbook, is published. (Having no competition, it stays on the best-seller lists for a little over a century.)

Notes

May						
S	M	T	W	T	F	S
30	1	2	3	4	5	6
7	8	9	10	11	12	13
14	15	16	17	18	19	20
21	22	23	24	25	26	27
28	29	30	31	1	2	3

Monday 8

Tuesday 9

Wednesday 10

Thursday 11

Friday 12

Saturday 13

Sunday 14

Mother's Day

May

Notes

S	M	T	W	T	F	S
30	1	2	3	4	5	6
7	8	9	10	11	12	13
14	15	16	17	18	19	20
21	22	23	24	25	26	27
28	29	30	31	1	2	3

May

Monday 15

Tuesday 16

Wednesday 17

Thursday 18

Friday 19

Saturday 20

Armed Forces Day
Sunday 21

"Did you detect something a little ominous
in the way they said, 'See you later'?"

May

1492
On Christmas Eve, the *Santa Maria*, piloted by a cabin boy, wrecks on the north coast of Hispaniola. Columbus takes control of the *Nina* and outraces the *Pinta* to be the first to arrive home with news of the New World. (The cabin boy is demoted to restroom boy.)

Notes

S	M	T	W	T	F	S
30	1	2	3	4	5	6
7	8	9	10	11	12	13
14	15	16	17	18	19	20
21	22	23	24	25	26	27
28	29	30	31	1	2	3

May

Monday 22

Victoria Day (Canada)

Tuesday 23

Wednesday 24

Thursday 25

Friday 26

Saturday 27

Sunday 28

June

Sunday	Monday	Tuesday	Wednesday	Thursday	Friday	Saturday
28	29	30	31	1	2	3
4	5	6	7	8	9	10
11	12	13	14 Flag Day	15	16	17
18 Father's Day	19	20	21	22	23	24
25	26	27	28	29	30	1

May

S	M	T	W	T	F	S
30	1	2	3	4	5	6
7	8	9	10	11	12	13
14	15	16	17	18	19	20
21	22	23	24	25	26	27
28	29	30	31	1	2	3

July

S	M	T	W	T	F	S
25	26	27	28	29	30	1
2	3	4	5	6	7	8
9	10	11	12	13	14	15
16	17	18	19	20	21	22
23	24	25	26	27	28	29
30	31					

Important Dates/Notes

May-June

Notes

			Monday			29

Memorial Day

Tuesday   30

Wednesday   31

Thursday   1

Friday   2

Saturday   3

Sunday   4

June

S	M	T	W	T	F	S
28	29	30	31	1	2	3
4	5	6	7	8	9	10
11	12	13	14	15	16	17
18	19	20	21	22	23	24
25	26	27	28	29	30	1

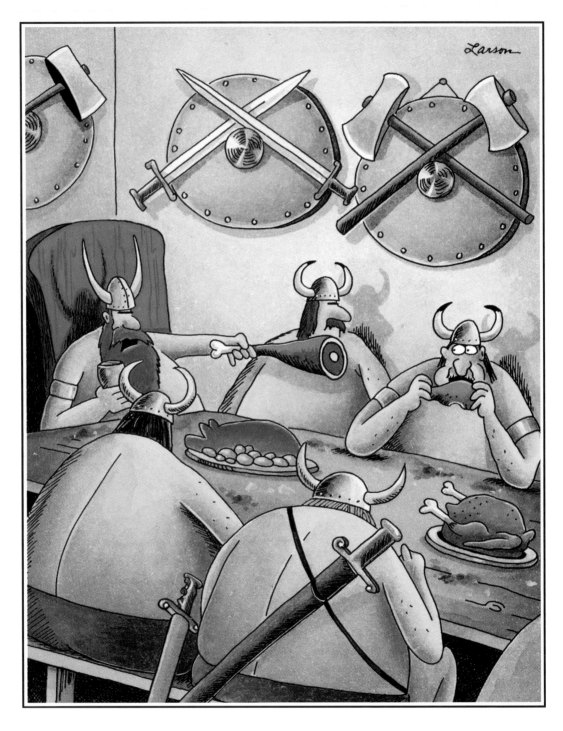

"Uh-uh-uh-uh-uh. ... Question. Can anyone here tell me what
Hanson there is doing wrong with his elbows?"

June

Notes

June						
S	M	T	W	T	F	S
28	29	30	31	1	2	3
4	5	6	7	8	9	10
11	12	13	14	15	16	17
18	19	20	21	22	23	24
25	26	27	28	29	30	1

Monday 5

Tuesday 6

Wednesday 7

Thursday 8

Friday 9

Saturday 10

Sunday 11

Sheep health classes

June

Notes

June

S	M	T	W	T	F	S
28	29	30	31	1	2	3
4	5	6	7	8	9	10
11	12	13	14	15	16	17
18	19	20	21	22	23	24
25	26	27	28	29	30	1

Monday 12

Tuesday 13

Wednesday 14

Flag Day
Thursday 15

Friday 16

Saturday 17

Sunday 18

Father's Day

"Hey! I got one! I got one!"

June

1550
Rodeos begin in what is now Mexico and the southwestern U.S. when cowboys—who come up with the inspired concept of a lasso—attempt to catch cows that escaped from a herd introduced by Columbus. (Around this same time, wild clowns are also captured and tamed, giving rise to the modern rodeo clown.)

Notes

_____

_____

_____

_____

_____

_____

_____

_____

_____

June

S	M	T	W	T	F	S
28	29	30	31	1	2	3
4	5	6	7	8	9	10
11	12	13	14	15	16	17
18	19	20	21	22	23	24
25	26	27	28	29	30	1

Monday 19

Tuesday 20

Wednesday 21

Thursday 22

Friday 23

Saturday 24

Sunday 25

July

Sunday	Monday	Tuesday	Wednesday	Thursday	Friday	Saturday
25	26	27	28	29	30	1 Canada Day
2	3	4 Independence Day	5	6	7	8
9	10	11	12	13	14	15
16	17	18	19	20	21	22
23	24	25	26	27	28	29
30	31					

June

S	M	T	W	T	F	S
28	29	30	31	1	2	3
4	5	6	7	8	9	10
11	12	13	14	15	16	17
18	19	20	21	22	23	24
25	26	27	28	29	30	1

August

S	M	T	W	T	F	S
30	31	1	2	3	4	5
6	7	8	9	10	11	12
13	14	15	16	17	18	19
20	21	22	23	24	25	26
27	28	29	30	31	1	2

Important Dates/Notes

June-July

1559
Ice cream appears in Italy when it's discovered that ice and salt make a cool combination.

Notes

July

S	M	T	W	T	F	S
25	26	27	28	29	30	1
2	3	4	5	6	7	8
9	10	11	12	13	14	15
16	17	18	19	20	21	22
23	24	25	26	27	28	29
30	31					

Monday 26

Tuesday 27

Wednesday 28

Thursday 29

Friday 30

Saturday 1

Canada Day
Sunday 2

July

1590
Dutch optician Zacharias Janssen invents the compound microscope, discovering that it's a small world after all.

Notes

July

S	M	T	W	T	F	S
25	26	27	28	29	30	1
2	3	4	5	6	7	8
9	10	11	12	13	14	15
16	17	18	19	20	21	22
23	24	25	26	27	28	29
30	31					

Monday   3

Tuesday   4

Wednesday   5

Thursday   6

Friday   7

Saturday   8

Sunday   9

"I tell ya, Ben—no matter who wins this thing,
Boot Hill ain't ever gonna be the same."

July

Notes

_____

_____

_____

_____

_____

_____

_____

_____

_____

July

S	M	T	W	T	F	S
25	26	27	28	29	30	1
2	3	4	5	6	7	8
9	10	11	12	13	14	15
16	17	18	19	20	21	22
23 30	24 31	25	26	27	28	29

Monday 10

Tuesday 11

Wednesday 12

Thursday 13

Friday 14

Saturday 15

Sunday 16

Hot off the press, the very first edition of the *Desert Island Times*
caused the newspaper to quickly fold.

July

Monday 17

Tuesday 18

Notes

Wednesday 19

Thursday 20

Friday 21

July

S	M	T	W	T	F	S
25	26	27	28	29	30	1
2	3	4	5	6	7	8
9	10	11	12	13	14	15
16	17	18	19	20	21	22
23 30	24 31	25	26	27	28	29

Saturday 22

Sunday 23

July

1610

Galileo improves the refractive telescope. His planetary theories fly in the face of religious dogma and he is forced to retract before the Inquisition. Nevertheless, he is imprisoned, and the validity of his scientific work is not formally recognized by the Roman Catholic Church until 1993. (Apparently, the Church wanted to make really, really sure Galileo knew what he was talking about.)

Notes

_____

_____

_____

_____

_____

_____

_____

July

S	M	T	W	T	F	S
25	26	27	28	29	30	1
2	3	4	5	6	7	8
9	10	11	12	13	14	15
16	17	18	19	20	21	22
23	24	25	26	27	28	29
30	31					

Monday 24

Tuesday 25

Wednesday 26

Thursday 27

Friday 28

Saturday 29

Sunday 30

August

Sunday	Monday	Tuesday	Wednesday	Thursday	Friday	Saturday
30	31	1	2	3	4	5
6	7	8	9	10	11	12
13	14	15	16	17	18	19
20	21	22	23	24	25	26
27	28	29	30	31	1	2

July

S	M	T	W	T	F	S
25	26	27	28	29	30	1
2	3	4	5	6	7	8
9	10	11	12	13	14	15
16	17	18	19	20	21	22
23	24	25	26	27	28	29
30	31					

September

S	M	T	W	T	F	S
27	28	29	30	31	1	2
3	4	5	6	7	8	9
10	11	12	13	14	15	16
17	18	19	20	21	22	23
24	25	26	27	28	29	30

Important Dates/Notes

July-August

1619

The story of the "Three Little Pigs" is introduced into English folklore.

Notes

August

S	M	T	W	T	F	S
30	31	1	2	3	4	5
6	7	8	9	10	11	12
13	14	15	16	17	18	19
20	21	22	23	24	25	26
27	28	29	30	31	1	2

Monday 31

Tuesday 1

Wednesday 2

Thursday 3

Friday 4

Saturday 5

Sunday 6

New York 1626: Chief of the Manhattan Indians addresses his tribe for the last time.

August

1626
The Dutch buy Manhattan.

Notes

August

S	M	T	W	T	F	S
30	31	1	2	3	4	5
6	7	8	9	10	11	12
13	14	15	16	17	18	19
20	21	22	23	24	25	26
27	28	29	30	31	1	2

Monday 7

Tuesday 8

Wednesday 9

Thursday 10

Friday 11

Saturday 12

Sunday 13

"Latte, Jed?"

August

1668
Coffee is introduced into America. (Tea becomes the official drink of "sissies.")

Notes

Monday	14
Tuesday	15
Wednesday	16
Thursday	17
Friday	18
Saturday	19
Sunday	20

August

S	M	T	W	T	F	S
30	31	1	2	3	4	5
6	7	8	9	10	11	12
13	14	15	16	17	18	19
20	21	22	23	24	25	26
27	28	29	30	31	1	2

In the animal self-help section

August

1704

The first library from which the public can check out books opens in Berlin. (A month after it opens, the first late fee is issued to one Wolfgang Muller.)

Notes

August

S	M	T	W	T	F	S
30	31	1	2	3	4	5
6	7	8	9	10	11	12
13	14	15	16	17	18	19
20	21	22	23	24	25	26
27	28	29	30	31	1	2

Monday   21

Tuesday   22

Wednesday   23

Thursday   24

Friday   25

Saturday   26

Sunday   27

September

Sunday	Monday	Tuesday	Wednesday	Thursday	Friday	Saturday
27	28	29	30	31	1	2
3	4 Labor Day	5	6	7	8	9
10	11	12	13	14	15	16
17	18	19	20	21	22	23
24	25	26	27	28	29	30 Rosh Hashanah

August

S	M	T	W	T	F	S
30	31	1	2	3	4	5
6	7	8	9	10	11	12
13	14	15	16	17	18	19
20	21	22	23	24	25	26
27	28	29	30	31	1	2

October

S	M	T	W	T	F	S
1	2	3	4	5	6	7
8	9	10	11	12	13	14
15	16	17	18	19	20	21
22	23	24	25	26	27	28
29	30	31	1	2	3	4

Important Dates/Notes

"So! Mr. Carlisle was right! ... I put you on a short leash so you can't harass him anymore, and *look* what you resort to!"

August-September

Monday   28

Tuesday   29

Notes

_____

_____

_____

_____

_____

_____

_____

_____

_____

Wednesday   30

Thursday   31

Friday   1

Saturday   2

September

S	M	T	W	T	F	S
27	28	29	30	31	1	2
3	4	5	6	7	8	9
10	11	12	13	14	15	16
17	18	19	20	21	22	23
24	25	26	27	28	29	30

Sunday   3

The Lone Ranger, long since retired, makes an unpleasant discovery.

September

1755

Dr. Samuel Johnson publishes his *Dictionary of the English Language*, the first comprehensive lexicographical work on English ever undertaken (finally enabling the world to spell "rhythm" and "receive").

Notes

September

S	M	T	W	T	F	S
27	28	29	30	31	1	2
3	4	5	6	7	8	9
10	11	12	13	14	15	16
17	18	19	20	21	22	23
24	25	26	27	28	29	30

Monday 4

Labor Day

Tuesday 5

Wednesday 6

Thursday 7

Friday 8

Saturday 9

Sunday 10

"Now this is ... this is ... well, I guess it's another snake."

September

1759

Etienne de Silhouette is appointed controller general of France. His brief tenure (he serves for a mere nine months) leads people to use his name as a synonym for "shadow."

Notes

September

S	M	T	W	T	F	S
27	28	29	30	31	1	2
3	4	5	6	7	8	9
10	11	12	13	14	15	16
17	18	19	20	21	22	23
24	25	26	27	28	29	30

Monday 11

Tuesday 12

Wednesday 13

Thursday 14

Friday 15

Saturday 16

Sunday 17

Slowly he would cruise the neighborhood, waiting for that occasional
careless child who confused him with another vendor.

September

1777

George Washington has the entire Continental army (at the time 4,000 strong) vaccinated against malaria. It quite possibly saves the army as a fighting force. (The inoculations are known to be painful, which helps explain why George is standing as he crosses the Delaware.)

Notes

Monday	18

Tuesday	19

Wednesday	20

Thursday	21

Friday	22

Saturday	23

Sunday	24

September

S	M	T	W	T	F	S
27	28	29	30	31	1	2
3	4	5	6	7	8	9
10	11	12	13	14	15	16
17	18	19	20	21	22	23
24	25	26	27	28	29	30

October

Sunday	Monday	Tuesday	Wednesday	Thursday	Friday	Saturday
1	2	3	4	5	6	7
8	9 Columbus Day Yom Kippur Thanksgiving (Canada)	10	11	12	13	14
15	16	17	18	19	20	21
22	23	24	25	26	27	28
29	30	31 Halloween	1	2	3	4

September

S	M	T	W	T	F	S
27	28	29	30	31	1	2
3	4	5	6	7	8	9
10	11	12	13	14	15	16
17	18	19	20	21	22	23
24	25	26	27	28	29	30

November

S	M	T	W	T	F	S
29	30	31	1	2	3	4
5	6	7	8	9	10	11
12	13	14	15	16	17	18
19	20	21	22	23	24	25
26	27	28	29	30	1	2

Important Dates/Notes

"Yes ... I believe there's a question in the back."

September-October

1785
Robert Bakewell begins experimenting with the cross-breeding of cows to enhance and create desirable characteristics. (He gets carried away, however, when he begins a quest for "deep, brown eyes—the kind you could just fall into.")

Notes

Monday	25

Tuesday	26

Wednesday	27

Thursday	28

Friday	29

Saturday	30

Rosh Hashanah

Sunday	1

October

S	M	T	W	T	F	S
1	2	3	4	5	6	7
8	9	10	11	12	13	14
15	16	17	18	19	20	21
22	23	24	25	26	27	28
29	30	31	1	2	3	4

Frog pioneers

October

Notes

October

S	M	T	W	T	F	S
1	2	3	4	5	6	7
8	9	10	11	12	13	14
15	16	17	18	19	20	21
22	23	24	25	26	27	28
29	30	31	1	2	3	4

Monday 2

Tuesday 3

Wednesday 4

Thursday 5

Friday 6

Saturday 7

Sunday 8

"You idiot! We want the scent *on* the pillow! On the pillow!"

October

1805

In England, a group called the Thrapthon Association for the Prevention of Felons acquires a bloodhound to help search for poachers and thieves. It is the breed's first recorded use by law enforcement (and replaces the Chihuahua, which—although a good tracker—is prone to being stepped on).

Notes

_____

_____

_____

_____

_____

_____

_____

_____

October

S	M	T	W	T	F	S
1	2	3	4	5	6	7
8	9	10	11	12	13	14
15	16	17	18	19	20	21
22	23	24	25	26	27	28
29	30	31	1	2	3	4

Monday — 9
Yom Kippur
Columbus Day
Thanksgiving (Canada)

Tuesday — 10

Wednesday — 11

Thursday — 12

Friday — 13

Saturday — 14

Sunday — 15

"OK, crybaby! You want the last soda? Well, let me GET IT READY FOR YOU!"

October

Notes

October

S	M	T	W	T	F	S
1	2	3	4	5	6	7
8	9	10	11	12	13	14
15	16	17	18	19	20	21
22	23	24	25	26	27	28
29	30	31	1	2	3	4

Monday 16

Tuesday 17

Wednesday 18

Thursday 19

Friday 20

Saturday 21

Sunday 22

"Any theories on this, Cummings?"

October

1821

Using the Rosetta Stone, Jean-Francois Champollion deciphers Egyptian hieroglyphs. (Others working on the same problem are heard to complain, "Oh, sure! He used the Rosetta Stone!")

Notes

October

S	M	T	W	T	F	S
1	2	3	4	5	6	7
8	9	10	11	12	13	14
15	16	17	18	19	20	21
22	23	24	25	26	27	28
29	30	31	1	2	3	4

Monday 23

Tuesday 24

Wednesday 25

Thursday 26

Friday 27

Saturday 28

Sunday 29

November

Sunday	Monday	Tuesday	Wednesday	Thursday	Friday	Saturday
29	30	31	1	2	3	4
5	6	7 Election Day	8	9	10	11 Veterans' Day Remembrance Day (Canada)
12	13	14	15	16	17	18
19	20	21	22	23 Thanksgiving	24	25
26	27	28	29	30	1	2

October

S	M	T	W	T	F	S
1	2	3	4	5	6	7
8	9	10	11	12	13	14
15	16	17	18	19	20	21
22	23	24	25	26	27	28
29	30	31	1	2	3	4

December

S	M	T	W	T	F	S
26	27	28	29	30	1	2
3	4	5	6	7	8	9
10	11	12	13	14	15	16
17	18	19	20	21	22	23
24 / 31	25	26	27	28	29	30

Important Dates/Notes

While their owners sleep, nervous little dogs prepare for their day.

October-November

1821

Caffeine is discovered by Pierre-Joseph Pelletier. It is known to contribute to irritability, depression, diarrhea, insomnia, and other disorders. (I'll take mine black.)

Notes

November

S	M	T	W	T	F	S
29	30	31	1	2	3	4
5	6	7	8	9	10	11
12	13	14	15	16	17	18
19	20	21	22	23	24	25
26	27	28	29	30	1	2

Monday 30

Tuesday 31

Halloween
Wednesday 1

Thursday 2

Friday 3

Saturday 4

Sunday 5

Front porch forecasters

November

Notes

_____

_____

_____

_____

_____

_____

_____

_____

_____

_____

_____

November

S	M	T	W	T	F	S
29	30	31	1	2	3	4
5	6	7	8	9	10	11
12	13	14	15	16	17	18
19	20	21	22	23	24	25
26	27	28	29	30	1	2

Monday 6

Tuesday 7

Election Day

Wednesday 8

Thursday 9

Friday 10

Saturday 11

Veterans' Day
Remembrance Day (Canada)

Sunday 12

"Hey, I'm not crazy. ... Sure, I let him drive once in a while, but he's never, *never* off this leash for even a second."

November

1905
The U.S. Automobile Association is formed. Its original mission is to provide "scouts" who will warn motorists (all 12 of them) of hidden police traps.

Notes

November

S	M	T	W	T	F	S
29	30	31	1	2	3	4
5	6	7	8	9	10	11
12	13	14	15	16	17	18
19	20	21	22	23	24	25
26	27	28	29	30	1	2

Monday 13

Tuesday 14

Wednesday 15

Thursday 16

Friday 17

Saturday 18

Sunday 19

"OK, let's see—that's a curse on you, a curse on you, and a curse on you."

November

Notes

November

S	M	T	W	T	F	S
29	30	31	1	2	3	4
5	6	7	8	9	10	11
12	13	14	15	16	17	18
19	20	21	22	23	24	25
26	27	28	29	30	1	2

Monday 20

Tuesday 21

Wednesday 22

Thursday 23

Thanksgiving
Friday 24

Saturday 25

Sunday 26

December

Sunday	Monday	Tuesday	Wednesday	Thursday	Friday	Saturday
26	27	28	29	30	1	2
3	4	5	6	7	8	9
10	11	12	13	14	15	16
17	18	19	20	21	22 Hanukkah	23
24 / 31	25 Christmas	26 Kwanzaa begins Boxing Day (Canada)	27	28	29	30

November

S	M	T	W	T	F	S
29	30	31	1	2	3	4
5	6	7	8	9	10	11
12	13	14	15	16	17	18
19	20	21	22	23	24	25
26	27	28	29	30	1	2

January 2001

S	M	T	W	T	F	S
31	1	2	3	4	5	6
7	8	9	10	11	12	13
14	15	16	17	18	19	20
21	22	23	24	25	26	27
28	29	30	31	1	2	3

Important Dates/Notes

"Oh my God, Bernie! You're wearing my nylon?"

November-December

1935
Nylon is developed by DuPont scientist Wallace Hume Carothers. (In stocking form, it flatters women's legs and provides bank robbers with a combination disguise and see-through product.)

WANTED

Notes

Monday	27

Tuesday	28

Wednesday	29

Thursday	30

Friday	1

Saturday	2

Sunday	3

December

S	M	T	W	T	F	S
26	27	28	29	30	1	2
3	4	5	6	7	8	9
10	11	12	13	14	15	16
17	18	19	20	21	22	23
24 31	25	26	27	28	29	30

March 16, 1942: The night before he leaves the Philippines,
Gen. MacArthur works on his farewell address.

December

Monday 4

Tuesday 5

Notes

_____

_____

_____

_____

_____

_____

_____

_____

Wednesday 6

Thursday 7

Friday 8

December

S	M	T	W	T	F	S
26	27	28	29	30	1	2
3	4	5	6	7	8	9
10	11	12	13	14	15	16
17	18	19	20	21	22	23
24 31	25	26	27	28	29	30

Saturday 9

Sunday 10

"Take another memo, Miss Wilkens. ... I want to see all reptile
personnel in my office first thing tomorrow morning!"

December

1963

Colossus, a 22-foot reticulated python, dies at Highland Park Zoo in Pennsylvania. She was the largest snake held in captivity up to that time. (Her coffin requires 18 pallbearers, also a record.)

Notes

December						
S	M	T	W	T	F	S
26	27	28	29	30	1	2
3	4	5	6	7	8	9
10	11	12	13	14	15	16
17	18	19	20	21	22	23
24 / 31	25	26	27	28	29	30

Monday 11

Tuesday 12

Wednesday 13

Thursday 14

Friday 15

Saturday 16

Sunday 17

"Make a note of this, Muldoon. ... The wounds seem to be caused by bird shot ... big bird shot."

December

Monday 18

Tuesday 19

Notes

Wednesday 20

Thursday 21

Friday 22

Hanukkah
Saturday 23

December

S	M	T	W	T	F	S
26	27	28	29	30	1	2
3	4	5	6	7	8	9
10	11	12	13	14	15	16
17	18	19	20	21	22	23
24 / 31	25	26	27	28	29	30

Sunday 24

"Hey, you stupid bovines! You'll never get that contraption off the ground! ...
Think it'll run on hay? ... Say, maybe you'll make it to the mooooooooon! ..."

December

1981
The first U.S. space shuttle is launched. The astronauts' first dinner on board includes thermostabilized irradiated beefsteak. (Mmmmmm...)

Notes

December

S	M	T	W	T	F	S
26	27	28	29	30	1	2
3	4	5	6	7	8	9
10	11	12	13	14	15	16
17	18	19	20	21	22	23
24 / 31	25	26	27	28	29	30

Monday 25

Christmas
Tuesday 26

Boxing Day (canada)
Kwanzaa begins
Wednesday 27

Thursday 28

Friday 29

Saturday 30

Sunday 31

January 2001

February

March

April

_____

_____

_____

_____

_____

May

_____

_____

_____

_____

_____

June

_____

_____

_____

_____

_____

July 2001

August

September

October

_____

_____

_____

_____

_____

_____

November

_____

_____

_____

_____

_____

_____

December

_____

_____

_____

_____

_____

_____

January 1999

S	M	T	W	T	F	S
27	28	29	30	31	1	2
3	4	5	6	7	8	9
10	11	12	13	14	15	16
17	18	19	20	21	22	23
24/31	25	26	27	28	29	30

February 1999

S	M	T	W	T	F	S
31	1	2	3	4	5	6
7	8	9	10	11	12	13
14	15	16	17	18	19	20
21	22	23	24	25	26	27
28	1	2	3	4	5	6

March 1999

S	M	T	W	T	F	S
28	1	2	3	4	5	6
7	8	9	10	11	12	13
14	15	16	17	18	19	20
21	22	23	24	25	26	27
28	29	30	31	1	2	3

April 1999

S	M	T	W	T	F	S
28	29	30	31	1	2	3
4	5	6	7	8	9	10
11	12	13	14	15	16	17
18	19	20	21	22	23	24
25	26	27	28	29	30	1

May 1999

S	M	T	W	T	F	S
25	26	27	28	29	30	1
2	3	4	5	6	7	8
9	10	11	12	13	14	15
16	17	18	19	20	21	22
23/30	24/31	25	26	27	28	29

June 1999

S	M	T	W	T	F	S
30	31	1	2	3	4	5
6	7	8	9	10	11	12
13	14	15	16	17	18	19
20	21	22	23	24	25	26
27	28	29	30	1	2	3

July 1999

S	M	T	W	T	F	S
27	28	29	30	1	2	3
4	5	6	7	8	9	10
11	12	13	14	15	16	17
18	19	20	21	22	23	24
25	26	27	28	29	30	31

August 1999

S	M	T	W	T	F	S
1	2	3	4	5	6	7
8	9	10	11	12	13	14
15	16	17	18	19	20	21
22	23	24	25	26	27	28
29	30	31	1	2	3	4

September 1999

S	M	T	W	T	F	S
29	30	31	1	2	3	4
5	6	7	8	9	10	11
12	13	14	15	16	17	18
19	20	21	22	23	24	25
26	27	28	29	30	1	2

October 1999

S	M	T	W	T	F	S
26	27	28	29	30	1	2
3	4	5	6	7	8	9
10	11	12	13	14	15	16
17	18	19	20	21	22	23
24/31	25	26	27	28	29	30

November 1999

S	M	T	W	T	F	S
31	1	2	3	4	5	6
7	8	9	10	11	12	13
14	15	16	17	18	19	20
21	22	23	24	25	26	27
28	29	30	1	2	3	4

December 1999

S	M	T	W	T	F	S
28	29	30	1	2	3	4
5	6	7	8	9	10	11
12	13	14	15	16	17	18
19	20	21	22	23	24	25
26	27	28	29	30	31	1

January 2000

S	M	T	W	T	F	S
26	27	28	29	30	31	1
2	3	4	5	6	7	8
9	10	11	12	13	14	15
16	17	18	19	20	21	22
23 / 30	24 / 31	25	26	27	28	29

February 2000

S	M	T	W	T	F	S
30	31	1	2	3	4	5
6	7	8	9	10	11	12
13	14	15	16	17	18	19
20	21	22	23	24	25	26
27	28	29	1	2	3	4

March 2000

S	M	T	W	T	F	S
27	28	29	1	2	3	4
5	6	7	8	9	10	11
12	13	14	15	16	17	18
19	20	21	22	23	24	25
26	27	28	29	30	31	1

April 2000

S	M	T	W	T	F	S
26	27	28	29	30	31	1
2	3	4	5	6	7	8
9	10	11	12	13	14	15
16	17	18	19	20	21	22
23 / 30	24	25	26	27	28	29

May 2000

S	M	T	W	T	F	S
30	1	2	3	4	5	6
7	8	9	10	11	12	13
14	15	16	17	18	19	20
21	22	23	24	25	26	27
28	29	30	31	1	2	3

June 2000

S	M	T	W	T	F	S
28	29	30	31	1	2	3
4	5	6	7	8	9	10
11	12	13	14	15	16	17
18	19	20	21	22	23	24
25	26	27	28	29	30	1

July 2000

S	M	T	W	T	F	S
25	26	27	28	29	30	1
2	3	4	5	6	7	8
9	10	11	12	13	14	15
16	17	18	19	20	21	22
23 / 30	24 / 31	25	26	27	28	29

August 2000

S	M	T	W	T	F	S
30	31	1	2	3	4	5
6	7	8	9	10	11	12
13	14	15	16	17	18	19
20	21	22	23	24	25	26
27	28	29	30	31	1	2

September 2000

S	M	T	W	T	F	S
27	28	29	30	31	1	2
3	4	5	6	7	8	9
10	11	12	13	14	15	16
17	18	19	20	21	22	23
24	25	26	27	28	29	30

October 2000

S	M	T	W	T	F	S
1	2	3	4	5	6	7
8	9	10	11	12	13	14
15	16	17	18	19	20	21
22	23	24	25	26	27	28
29	30	31	1	2	3	4

November 2000

S	M	T	W	T	F	S
29	30	31	1	2	3	4
5	6	7	8	9	10	11
12	13	14	15	16	17	18
19	20	21	22	23	24	25
26	27	28	29	30	1	2

December 2000

S	M	T	W	T	F	S
26	27	28	29	30	1	2
3	4	5	6	7	8	9
10	11	12	13	14	15	16
17	18	19	20	21	22	23
24 / 31	25	26	27	28	29	30

January 2001

S	M	T	W	T	F	S
31	1	2	3	4	5	6
7	8	9	10	11	12	13
14	15	16	17	18	19	20
21	22	23	24	25	26	27
28	29	30	31	1	2	3

February 2001

S	M	T	W	T	F	S
28	29	30	31	1	2	3
4	5	6	7	8	9	10
11	12	13	14	15	16	17
18	19	20	21	22	23	24
25	26	27	28	1	2	3

March 2001

S	M	T	W	T	F	S
25	26	27	28	1	2	3
4	5	6	7	8	9	10
11	12	13	14	15	16	17
18	19	20	21	22	23	24
25	26	27	28	29	30	31

April 2001

S	M	T	W	T	F	S
1	2	3	4	5	6	7
8	9	10	11	12	13	14
15	16	17	18	19	20	21
22	23	24	25	26	27	28
29	30	1	2	3	4	5

May 2001

S	M	T	W	T	F	S
29	30	1	2	3	4	5
6	7	8	9	10	11	12
13	14	15	16	17	18	19
20	21	22	23	24	25	26
27	28	29	30	31	1	2

June 2001

S	M	T	W	T	F	S
27	28	29	30	31	1	2
3	4	5	6	7	8	9
10	11	12	13	14	15	16
17	18	19	20	21	22	23
24	25	26	27	28	29	30

July 2001

S	M	T	W	T	F	S
1	2	3	4	5	6	7
8	9	10	11	12	13	14
15	16	17	18	19	20	21
22	23	24	25	26	27	28
29	30	31	1	2	3	4

August 2001

S	M	T	W	T	F	S
29	30	31	1	2	3	4
5	6	7	8	9	10	11
12	13	14	15	16	17	18
19	20	21	22	23	24	25
26	27	28	29	30	31	1

September 2001

S	M	T	W	T	F	S
26	27	28	29	30	31	1
2	3	4	5	6	7	8
9	10	11	12	13	14	15
16	17	18	19	20	21	22
23 / 30	24	25	26	27	28	29

October 2001

S	M	T	W	T	F	S
30	1	2	3	4	5	6
7	8	9	10	11	12	13
14	15	16	17	18	19	20
21	22	23	24	25	26	27
28	29	30	31	1	2	3

November 2001

S	M	T	W	T	F	S
28	29	30	31	1	2	3
4	5	6	7	8	9	10
11	12	13	14	15	16	17
18	19	20	21	22	23	24
25	26	27	28	29	30	

December 2001

S	M	T	W	T	F	S
25	26	27	28	29	30	1
2	3	4	5	6	7	8
9	10	11	12	13	14	15
16	17	18	19	20	21	22
23 / 30	24 / 31	25	26	27	28	29

Names & Numbers

Names & Numbers